Look Out!

and

Dot and Dan's Trip

By Katie Dale

Illustrated by
Dean Gray

The Letter T

Trace the lower and upper case letter with a finger. Sound out the letter.

Down,
lift,
cross

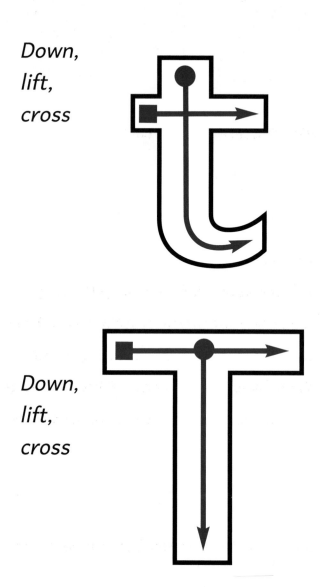

Down,
lift,
cross

Some words to familiarise:

tiptoe   look   Dan

High-frequency words:

the

Tips for Reading 'Look Out!'

- Practise the words listed above before reading the story.

- If the reader struggles with any of the other words, ask them to look for sounds they know in the word. Encourage them to sound out the words and help them read the words if necessary.

- After reading the story, ask the reader what happens to the cat in the end.

Fun Activity

Discuss what Dot and Dan will have to look out for next time.

Look Out!

Tiptoe past the bed.

Look out Dan!

Tiptoe past the mug.

Look out Dan!

Tiptoe past the cat.

Look out Dan!

Tiptoe past the mop.

Look out Dan!

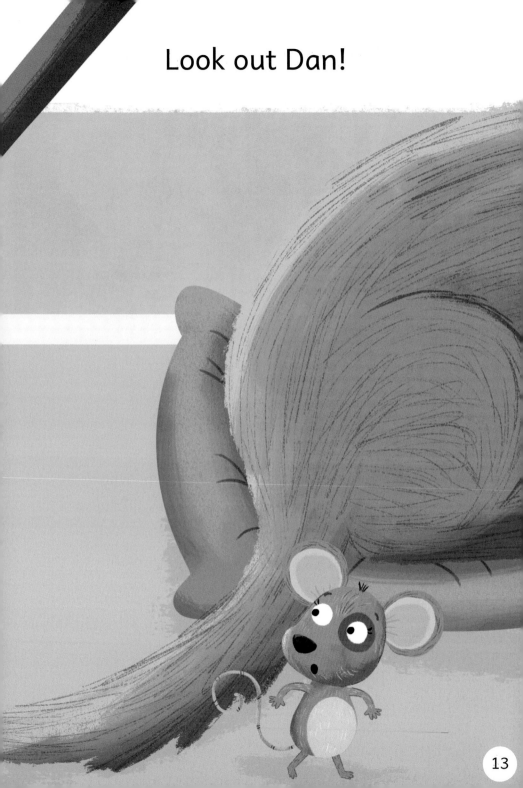

Tiptoe past the dog.

Look out Dan!

Look out cat!

The Letter D

Trace the lower and upper case letter with a finger. Sound out the letter.

Around,
up,
down

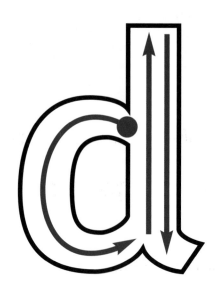

Down,
up,
around

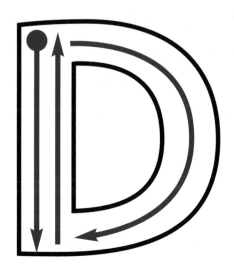

Some words to familiarise:

boat   train   plane

High-frequency words:

a go on

Tips for Reading 'Dot and Dan's Trip'

- Practise the words listed above before reading the story.

- If the reader struggles with any of the other words, ask them to look for sounds they know in the word. Encourage them to sound out the words and help them read the words if necessary.

- After reading the story, ask the reader how Dan kept losing his cheese.

Fun Activity

Discuss why Dan is so happy to be home.

Dot and Dan's Trip

Dot and Dan go on a bus.

LONDON

Dot and Dan go on a boat.

24

Dot and Dan go on a plane.

Dot and Dan go on a train.

Dot and Dan go on a car.

Book Bands for Guided Reading

The Institute of Education book banding system is a scale of colours that reflects the various levels of reading difficulty. The bands are assigned by taking into account the content, the language style, the layout and phonics. Word, phrase and sentence level work is also taken into consideration.

Maverick Early Readers are a bright, attractive range of books covering the pink to white bands. All of these books have been book banded for guided reading to the industry standard and edited by a leading educational consultant.

To view the whole Maverick Readers scheme, visit our website at

www.maverickearlyreaders.com

Or scan the QR code above to view our scheme instantly!